MW00633165

Year A Student Notebook

THIS PRODUCT IS INTENDED FOR HOME USE ONLY

The images and all other content in this book are copyrighted material owned by Elemental Science, Inc. Please do not reproduce this content on email lists or websites. If you have an eBook, you may print out as many copies as you need for use WITHIN YOUR IMMEDIATE FAMILY ONLY. Duplicating this book or printing the eBook so that the book can then be reused or resold is a violation of copyright.

Schools and co-ops: You MAY NOT DUPLICATE OR PRINT any portion of this book for use in the classroom. Please contact us for licensing options at support@elementalscience.com.

Science Chunks - Year A Notebook

First Edition 2021

ISBN: 978-1-953490-08-7

Copyright @ Elemental Science, Inc.
Email: support@elementalscience.com

Copyright Policy

All contents copyright © 2021 by Elemental Science. All rights reserved.

Limit of Liability and Disclaimer of Warranty: The publisher has used its best efforts in preparing this book, and the information provided herein is provided "as is." Elemental Science makes no representation or warranties with respect to the accuracy or completeness of the contents of this book and specifically disclaims any implied warranties of merchantability or fitness for any particular purpose and shall in no event be liable for any loss of profit or any other commercial damage, including but not limited to special, incidental, consequential, or other damages.

Trademarks: This book identifies product names and services known to be trademarks, registered trademarks, or service marks of their respective holders. They are used throughout this book in an editorial fashion only. In addition, terms suspected of being trademarks, registered trademarks, or service marks have been appropriately capitalized, although Elemental Science cannot attest to the accuracy of this information. Use of a term in this book should not be regarded as affecting the validity of any trademark, registered trademark, or service mark. Elemental Science is not associated with any product or vendor mentioned in this book.

Table of Contents

Plants Unit

Leaves

Leaves

_____
_____
_____
_____
_____
_____
_____
_____
_____
_____
_____

Photosynthesis

_____
_____
_____
_____
_____
_____
_____
_____
_____
_____
_____

Flowers

Flowering Plants

_____
_____
_____
_____
_____
_____
_____

Flowers

_____
_____
_____
_____
_____
_____
_____

Pollen

_____
_____
_____
_____
_____
_____
_____

Fruit and Seeds

Fruit

_____

_____

_____

_____

_____

_____

_____

_____

_____

_____

_____

Seeds

_____

_____

_____

_____

_____

_____

_____

_____

_____

_____

Spores and Cones

Seedless Plants

_____

_____

_____

_____

_____

_____

_____

_____

_____

_____

_____

_____

Conifers

_____

_____

_____

_____

_____

_____

_____

_____

_____

_____

_____

_____

Stems

Stems

_____
_____
_____
_____
_____
_____
_____
_____
_____
_____
_____
_____

Plant Cells

_____
_____
_____
_____
_____
_____
_____
_____
_____
_____
_____
_____

Roots

Roots

_____
_____
_____
_____
_____
_____
_____

_____
_____
_____

Types of Roots

_____
_____
_____
_____
_____
_____
_____
_____

_____
_____
_____
_____

Mendel Unit

Gregor Mendel - His Life

Gregor Mendel - His Work

Mendel

The Father of Modern Genetics

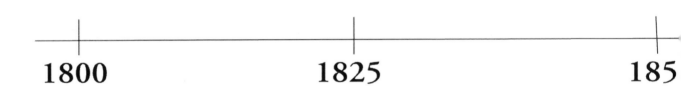

1800   1825   185

1875

1900

SCIENCE CHUNKS

Major Biomes Unit

Polar Biome

_____

_____

_____

_____

_____

_____

_____

_____

_____

_____

_____

_____

_____

_____

_____

_____

Forest Biome

_____
_____
_____
_____
_____
_____
_____
_____
_____
_____
_____
_____
_____
_____
_____
_____
_____
_____

Grasslands Biome

_____

_____

_____

_____

_____

_____

_____

_____

_____

_____

_____

_____

_____

_____

_____

_____

_____

_____

Desert Biome

_____

_____

_____

_____

_____

_____

_____

_____

_____

_____

_____

_____

_____

_____

_____

_____

_____

_____

Aquatic Biome

_____

_____

_____

_____

_____

_____

_____

_____

_____

_____

_____

_____

_____

_____

_____

_____

_____

_____

_____

_____

SCIENCE CHUNKS

Solar System Unit

The Solar System

The Milky Way

_____
_____
_____
_____
_____
_____
_____
_____
_____
_____

_____
_____
_____

Our Solar System

_____
_____
_____
_____
_____
_____
_____
_____
_____
_____
_____
_____

The Sun

_____

_____

_____

_____

_____

_____

_____

_____

_____

_____

_____

_____

_____

_____

Mercury

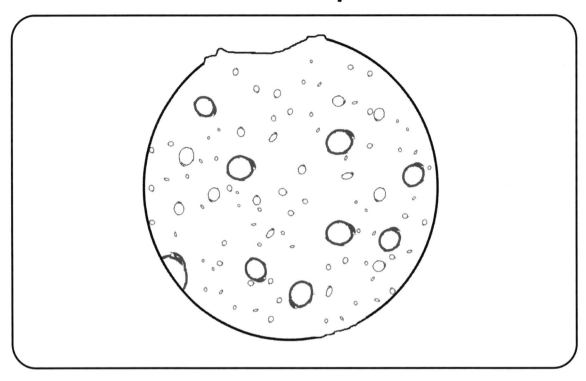

_____

_____

_____

_____

_____

_____

_____

_____

_____

_____

_____

_____

_____

Venus

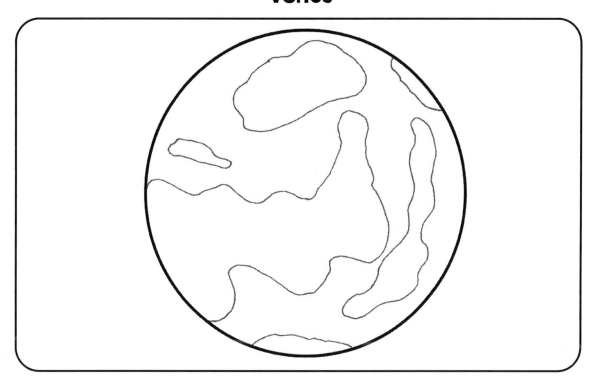

_____

_____

_____

_____

_____

_____

_____

_____

_____

_____

_____

_____

Earth and the Moon

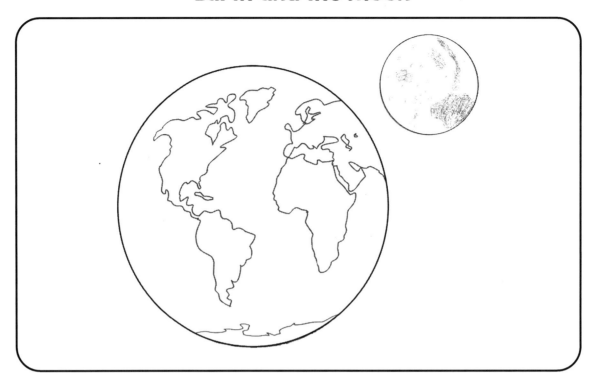

_____

_____

_____

_____

_____

_____

_____

_____

_____

_____

_____

_____

_____

_____

Mars

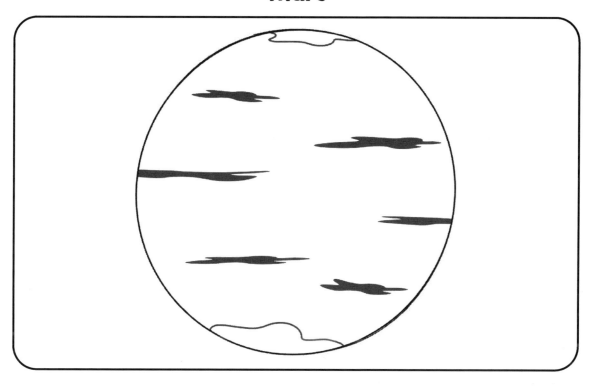

Jupiter

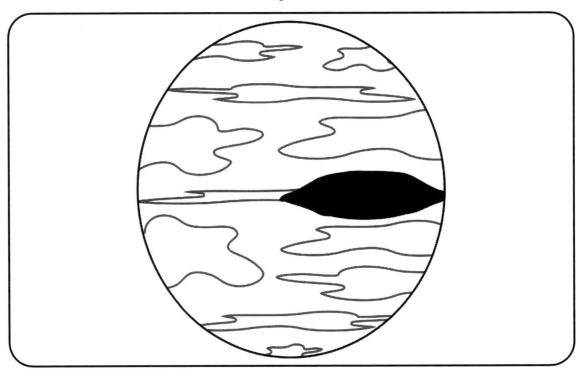

_____

_____

_____

_____

_____

_____

_____

_____

_____

_____

_____

_____

_____

Saturn

_____

_____

_____

_____

_____

_____

_____

_____

_____

_____

_____

_____

_____

_____

_____

_____

_____

_____

Uranus

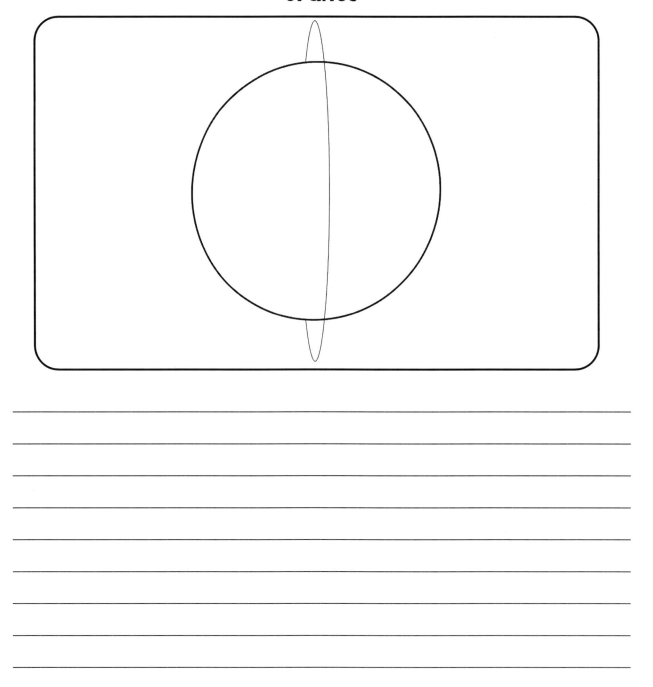

_____
_____
_____
_____
_____
_____
_____
_____
_____
_____
_____
_____
_____
_____

Neptune

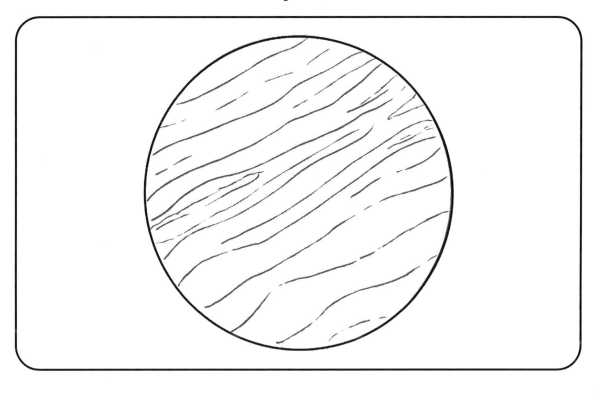

_____

_____

_____

_____

_____

_____

_____

_____

_____

_____

_____

_____

_____

Dwarf Planets

_____
_____
_____
_____
_____
_____
_____
_____
_____
_____
_____
_____
_____
_____
_____

Asteroids, Comets, and Meteors

Asteroid Belt

_____

_____

_____

_____

_____

_____

_____

Comet

_____

_____

_____

_____

_____

_____

_____

Meteors

_____

_____

_____

_____

_____

_____

_____

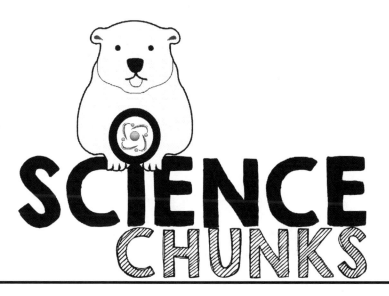

SCIENCE CHUNKS

Atoms and Molecules Unit

Atoms

Subatomic Particles

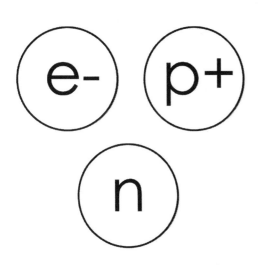

_____

_____

_____

_____

_____

_____

_____

Atoms

_____

_____

_____

_____

_____

_____

_____

_____

Isotopes

_____

_____

_____

_____

_____

_____

_____

Molecules

Electron Shells

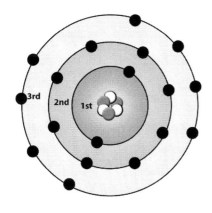

_____ electrons   fit   in   the   first   shell.

_____ electrons   fit   in   the   second   shell.

_____ electrons   fit   in   the   third   shell.

Molecules

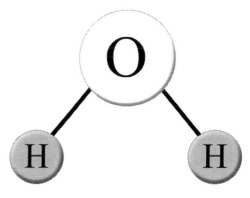

_____

_____

_____

_____

_____

_____

_____

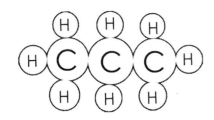

Polar and Nonpolar

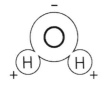

_____

_____

_____

_____

_____

_____

_____

Air

Air

_____
_____
_____
_____
_____
_____
_____

Oxygen

_____
_____
_____
_____
_____
_____
_____

8
O
Oxygen
16.00

Carbon Dioxide

_____
_____
_____
_____
_____
_____
_____

Water

Water

_____
_____
_____
_____
_____
_____
_____

Water as a Solvent

_____
_____
_____
_____
_____
_____
- - - - - - - - - - - - - - - - -

Hard Water

_____
_____
_____
_____
_____
_____
_____
_____

SCIENCE CHUNKS

Light Unit

Light

_____

_____

_____

_____

_____

_____

_____

_____

_____

_____

_____

_____

_____

_____

_____

_____

_____

_____

_____

_____

Colors

_____
_____
_____
_____
_____
_____
_____
_____
_____
_____
_____
_____
_____
_____
_____
_____
_____
_____

Light Unit Notebooking Pages

Light Behavior

_____
_____
_____
_____
_____
_____
_____
_____
_____
_____
_____
_____
_____
_____
_____
_____
_____
_____
_____
_____

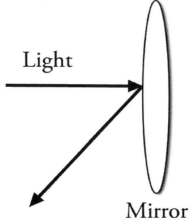

Mirror

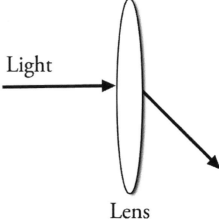

Lens

Lenses and Mirrors

_____

_____

_____

_____

_____

_____

_____

_____

_____

_____

_____

_____

_____

_____

_____

                                    _____

                                    _____

                                    _____

                                    _____

                                    _____

                                    _____

                                    _____

                                    _____

                                    _____

Sound Unit

Sound

_____
_____
_____
_____
_____
_____
_____
_____
_____
_____
_____
_____
_____
_____
_____
_____
_____
_____
_____

_____
_____
_____
_____
_____
_____
_____
_____

Waves

_____
_____
_____
_____
_____
_____
_____
_____
_____
_____
_____
_____
_____
_____
_____
_____
_____
_____
_____
_____
_____

Wave Behavior

_____
_____
_____
_____
_____
_____
_____
_____
_____
_____
_____
_____
_____
_____
_____
_____
_____
_____
_____
_____

_____
_____
_____
_____
_____
_____
_____

Musical Instruments

_____

_____

_____

_____

_____

_____

_____

_____

_____

_____

_____

_____

_____

_____

_____

_____

_____

_____

_____

Glossary

Year A Glossary

A

Air —

Aquatic Biome —

Asteroid —

Atmoshpere —

B

Biome —

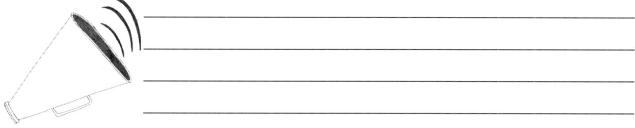

_____
_____
_____
_____

Bud —

_____
_____
_____
_____

C

Cone —

_____
_____
_____
_____

D

Decibel (dB) —

_____
_____
_____
_____

Desert —

_____
_____
_____
_____

Dominant Trait —

_____
_____
_____
_____

Drought —

_____
_____
_____
_____

Dwarf Planet —

_____
_____
_____
_____

E

Electron —

_____

_____

_____

_____

Electron Shell —

_____

_____

_____

_____

F

Flower —

_____

_____

_____

_____

Forest —

_____

_____

_____

_____

G

Genetic Trait —

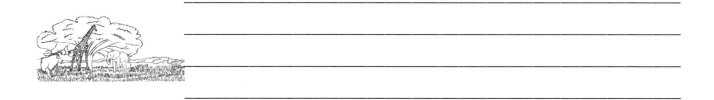

Grassland —

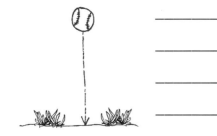

Gravity —

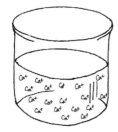

H

Hard Water —

Hybrid —

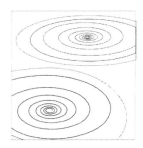

_____

_____

_____

_____

I

Interference —

_____

_____

_____

_____

Isotope —

Cl_{18n}
17
Chlorine
35

Cl_{20n}
17
Chlorine
37

_____

_____

_____

_____

J

K

L

Leaf —

_____

_____

_____

_____

Lens —

_____
_____
_____
_____

Light —

_____
_____
_____
_____

Longitudinal Wave —

_____
_____
_____
_____

M

Meteor —

_____
_____
_____
_____

Mirror —

_____
_____
_____
_____

Molecule —

_____
_____
_____
_____

Moon —

_____
_____
_____
_____

N

Neutron —

_____
_____
_____
_____

O

Orbit —

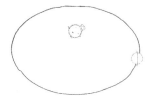

_____
_____
_____
_____

P

Planet —

_____
_____
_____
_____

Polar Biome —

_____
_____
_____
_____

Primary colors —

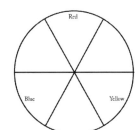

_____
_____
_____
_____

Proton —

p+

Q

R

Recessive Trait —

	T	T
T	TT	TT
t	Tt	Tt

Reflection —

Light

Mirror

Refraction —

Light

Lens

Resonate —

_____
_____
_____
_____

Roots —

_____
_____
_____
_____

S

Seconadary Colors —

_____
_____
_____
_____

Seed —

_____
_____
_____
_____

Shadow —

_____

_____

_____

_____

Solar system —

_____

_____

_____

_____

Solar wind —

_____

_____

_____

_____

Sound Wave —

_____

_____

_____

_____

Stem —

_____
_____
_____
_____

T

Temperate Zone —

_____
_____
_____
_____

Transverse Wave —

_____
_____
_____
_____

Tropical Zone —

_____
_____
_____
_____

U, V, W, X, Y, Z

Made in the USA
Columbia, SC
21 April 2022

59214555R00039